Seriously, CINDERELLA SO ANNOYING!

The story of
CINDERELLA
as told by THE WICKED STEPMOTHER

by Trisha Shaskan   illustrated by Gerald Guerlais

intree

www.raintreepublishers.co.uk
Visit our website to find out
more information about
Raintree books.

To order:
☎ Phone 0845 6044371
📠 Fax +44 (0) 1865 312263
✉ Email myorders@raintreepublishers.co.uk

Customers from outside the UK please telephone +44 1865 312262

Raintree is an imprint of Capstone Global Library Limited, a company incorporated in
England and Wales having its registered office at 7 Pilgrim Street, London, EC4V 6LB
– Registered company number: 6695582

Text © Picture Window Books 2012
First published in the United Kingdom in 2012
The moral rights of the proprietor have been asserted.

We would like to thank Terry Flaherty, Professor of English at Minnesota State
University, for his advice and expertise.

Editors: Jill Kalz and Vaarunika Dharmapala
Designer: Lori Bye
Art Director: Nathan Gassman
Production Specialist: Sarah Bennett
The illustrations in this book were created digitally.

ISBN 978 1 406 24311 6 (paperback)
16 15 14 13 12
10 9 8 7 6 5 4 3 2

British Library Cataloguing in Publication Data
A full catalogue record for this book is available from the British Library.

You must have heard of me. The *wicked* stepmother? That's not true. It's just another one of Cinderella's wild stories. Not as wild as the one about the pumpkin, or the one about the fairy godmother. The *real* story, the *true* story, began with some chatter — and some dust.

All I ever wanted was a husband and a mansion. Before I married Cindy's father, my two darlings and I had met Cindy only a few times. The girl had *seemed* normal then.

After I married Cindy's father, my darlings and I moved in. When I had just one foot on the front step, my dear husband kissed me goodbye and said, "I'm off on business!"

"He's often away," Cindy said, "but the animals stay put. They talk. They joke. They sing. They even help out — especially the bluebirds."

4

Now, I don't mind a good story but I do prefer facts to fiction. Soon, the girl was talking all kinds of nonsense.

"Once upon a time," Cindy said, "one of the bluebirds became blue. Not the colour. The feeling. His friend had flown south …"

My darlings and I were stuck near the front door. I just wanted to put away my bags. That's when I saw it: dust.

"Dear, is the whole house this dusty?" I asked.

"I don't know," Cindy said. "I'll give you a tour!"

In the dining room,
Cindy told stories.

In the study, Cindy told stories.

Non-stop.

"Girls," I said, "time to get to work. This place needs a good cleaning."

"Once upon a time, when I was cleaning …" Cindy started.

Oh, dear.

Cindy mopped the floor. She finished so fast! My darlings had barely started.

"Did you know robins and sparrows are my friends?" she said. "The sparrows don't like the robins, though. Silly creatures! Once upon a time, one of the robins –"

"Cindy, dear," I said, "why don't you go and wash the clothes now, hmm?"

Cindy washed them so fast! How on earth did she do it? I had to find another chore for her, just to keep her busy.

"If there's one thing squirrels love, it's washing clothes," Cindy said. "The rats, though, would rather iron. You know, one day I —"

"Squirrels and rats doing laundry? Stop telling such foolish stories!" I finally said.

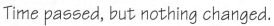

Time passed, but nothing changed.

In the garden, Cindy
told stories.

In the kitchen, Cindy told stories.

At dinner, I couldn't hear myself think.
"Dear, please," I said,

"STOP TALKING!"

Cindy didn't stop.

One day, a letter arrived. It was an invitation to the king's ball. The prince would surely fall in love with one of my darlings. Then they would marry, live in a beautiful castle, and one day be king and queen of all the land!

"Oh, Stepmother, I want to go, too!" said Cindy. "Once upon a time, a girl and a prince …"

Then – just like that – Cindy lost her voice. Imagine! It had to be from all that storytelling.

Well, what could I do? I told Cindy she had to stay at home for her health. She cried, of course. Still, a ball was no place for a poorly girl. She needed rest.

Sometimes, it's so hard being a stepmother.

15

At the ball, my darlings twirled. They whirled.

Then a strange girl waltzed in. Her gown was magnificent. I couldn't take my eyes off it. I wondered how much it had cost and if my seamstress could copy it for me.

The prince and the girl danced and pranced. My poor darlings were left prince-less.

A few days later, the prince made an announcement.
A glass slipper had been left at the castle. The prince
would marry the girl whose foot it fitted. Our big chance!

After visiting every other mansion in the city, the
prince's footman arrived at our door.

"Me! Me!" said one of my darlings.

"No, me! Me!" said the other.

"One at a time," said the footman.

18

Each girl tried, but the shoe didn't fit.

Then Cindy croaked out a whisper.
"Please – let – me – try."

The shoe fitted! Cindy pulled out the other glass shoe from her apron pocket.

"Whaaaaaat?" my darlings cried.

Cindy croaked again. She said something about a "pumpkin coach" and "mice that turned into horses". She even added a "fairy godmother". Please! There's no such thing!

I must say, though, I still don't know where she got those shoes ...

A few days later, the prince married Cindy. Poor man. He had no idea what he was getting himself into. We, on the other hand, lived happily ever after!

Think about it

Read a classic version of *Cinderella*. Now look at the stepmother's version of the story. List some things that happened in the classic version that did not happen in the stepmother's version. Then list some things that happened in the stepmother's version that did not happen in the classic. How are the two stories different?

Most versions of *Cinderella* tend to be told from an invisible narrator's point of view. This version is from the stepmother's point of view. Which point of view do you think is more honest? Why?

If you could be one of the main characters in this version of *Cinderella*, who would you be, and why? The stepmother or one of the stepsisters? Cinderella? The prince?

How would other fairy tales change if they were told from another point of view? For example, how would *Hansel and Gretel* change if the witch was the narrator? What if Baby Bear in *Goldilocks and the Three Bears* told that story? Write your own version of a classic fairy tale from a new point of view.

⚬⚬❧❀❧⚬⚬

Glossary

character person, animal, or creature in a story

narrator person who tells a story

point of view way of looking at something

version account of something from a certain point of view

Books in this series:

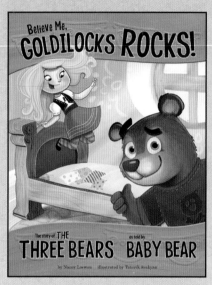

978 1 406 24309 3

978 1 406 24310 9

978 1 406 24311 6

978 1 406 24312 3